To our Becky,

Christmas 1966

love, Gram and Gramp U.

The Very Young

MOTHER GOOSE

Illustrated by Margot Austin

PLATT & MUNK, *Publishers* • **NEW YORK**

About Mother Goose

MOTHER GOOSE first appeared in Europe over three hundred years ago. Where she came from nobody knows, although many theories have been advanced to explain her origin. She has been mentioned in many countries and portrayed as a kindly old mother, nanny or noblewoman. Some scholars trace her back to an ancient queen who in some churches is honored as the patron saint of children. Others find her origin in Elizabeth Vergoose of Boston.

Charles Perrault first linked her name to *Cinderella, Puss in Boots,* and other favorite fairy tales when he published his *Stories of My Mother Goose* in France in 1697. In England a few years later she became the "authoress" of innumerable rhymes, some of them folk rhymes, some political satires.

By the nineteenth century Mother Goose had become the familiar figure of the nursery world whom all of us know and love as the one who first introduced us to the fascinating world of word sounds and patterns. The hundreds of ditties, riddles, songs, limericks and jingles that make up Mother Goose rhymes are known as nursery rhymes in England. But in America the kindly old lady in the peaked hat still leads children to the early joys of Pat-a-Cake, Jack Be Nimble, Little Boy Blue and a colorful host of characters and verses. So the children of today's space age find in these lively rhymes the same pleasure and recognition that millions of other children found in a quieter age.

To every child of this new day, the publishers offer this collection of timeless rhymes, appropriately illustrated by Margot Austin and appropriately entitled, *The Very Young Mother Goose.*

Contents

LITTLE BOY BLUE, COME BLOW YOUR HORN

DAFFY-DOWN-DILLY

Daffy-down-dilly has come up to town,
In a yellow petticoat and a green gown.

I WENT UP ONE PAIR OF STAIRS

"I went up one pair of stairs."
 "Just like me."
"I went up two pair of stairs."
 "Just like me."
"I went into a room."
 "Just like me."
"I looked out a window."
 "Just like me."
"And there I saw a monkey."
 "Just like me!!!"

IF I HAD A PONY

If I had a pony and he would not go,
Do you think I'd whip him?
 No, no, no!
I'd say "Gee-up pony,"
And away he'd go.

LITTLE BOY BLUE

Little Boy Blue, come blow your horn,
The sheep's in the meadow, the cow's in the corn;
But where is the little boy who looks after the sheep?
He's under the haystack fast asleep.
Will you wake him? No, not I!
For if I do, he's sure to cry.

LITTLE ROBIN REDBREAST SAT UPON A TREE

Little Robin Redbreast sat upon a
    tree,
Up went Pussy cat, and down
    went he;
Down came Pussy cat, and away
    Robin ran;
Says little Robin Redbreast,
    "Catch me if you can."

THERE'S A NEAT LITTLE CLOCK

There's a neat little clock—
In the schoolroom it stands—
And it points to the time
With its two little hands.

And may we, like the clock,
Keep a face clean and bright,
With hands ever ready
To do what is right.

I AM A GOLD KEY

I am a gold lock.
    I am a gold key.
I am a silver lock.
    I am a silver key.
I am a brass lock.
    I am a brass key.
I am a lead lock.
    I am a lead key.
I am a monk lock.
    I am a monk key!

LITTLE BO-PEEP

Little Bo-Peep has lost her sheep,
    And can't tell where to find
    them;
Leave them alone, and they'll
    come home,
    And bring their tails behind
    them.

Little Bo-Peep fell fast asleep,
    And dreamt she heard them
    bleating;
But when she awoke, she found
    it a joke,
    For they still were all fleeting.

Then up she took her little crook,
    Determined for to find them;
What was her joy to behold them
    nigh,
    Wagging their tails behind
    them.

LITTLE BO-PEEP HAS LOST HER SHEEP

15

IF I WERE AN APPLE

If I were an apple
    And grew on a tree,
I think I'd drop down
    On a nice boy like me.

I wouldn't stay there
    Giving nobody joy;
I'd fall down at once
    And say, "Eat me, my boy!"

GOOSEY, GOOSEY, GANDER

Goosey, goosey, gander,
Where shall I wander?
Upstairs, downstairs,
In my lady's chamber.
There I met an old man
Who would not say his prayers;
I took him by the left leg,
And threw him downstairs.

IF ALL THE WORLD WERE APPLE PIE

If all the world were apple pie
    And all the sea were ink,
And all the trees were bread and
        cheese,
    What should we have to
        drink?
It's enough to make an old man
    Scratch his head and think.

MARY HAD A LITTLE LAMB

Mary had a little lamb,
    Its fleece was white as snow;
And everywhere that Mary went
    The lamb was sure to go.

It followed her to school one day,
    That was against the rule;
It made the children laugh and
        play,
    To see a lamb at school.

And so the teacher turned it out,
    But still it lingered near;
And waited patiently about
    Till Mary did appear.

"Why does the lamb love Mary
        so?"
    The eager children cry;
"Why, Mary loves the lamb, you
        know!"
    The teacher did reply.

16

MARY HAD A LITTLE LAMB

I HAD A LITTLE COW

I had a little cow; to save her,
I turned her into the meadow to
  graze her:
There came a heavy storm of
  rain,
And drove the little cow home
  again.

The church doors they stood open,
And there the little cow was
  cropen;
The bell-ropes they were made of
  hay,
And the little cow ate them all
  away:
The sexton came to toll the bell,
And pushed the little cow into
  the well!

A SUNSHINY SHOWER

A sunshiny shower
Won't last half an hour.

THE FIVE TOES

1. "Let us go to the woods," says
    this pig;
2. "What to do there?" says that
    pig;
3. "To look for mother," says
    this pig;
4. "What to do with her?" says
    that pig;
5. "To kiss her, to kiss her,"
    says this pig.

WILLY BOY, WILLY BOY

"Willy boy, Willy boy, where
  are you going?
  I will go with you, if I may."
"I'm going to the meadow, to see
  them a-mowing,
I'm going to help them make the
  hay."

THE QUEEN OF HEARTS

The Queen of Hearts
She made some tarts,
   All on a summer's day,
The Knave of Hearts
He stole those tarts,
   And took them clean away.

The King of Hearts
Called for the tarts,
   And beat the Knave full sore;
The Knave of Hearts
Brought back the tarts,
   And vowed he'd steal no more.

RUB-A-DUB-DUB

Rub-a-dub-dub,—
Three men in a tub,
And who do you think they be?
The butcher, the baker,
The candle-stick maker,
Turn 'em out, knaves all three.

ROCK-A-BY, BABY

Rock-a-by, baby, thy cradle is
    green;
Father's a nobleman, mother's a
    queen;
And Betty's a lady, and wears a
    gold ring;
And Johnny's a drummer and
    drums for the king.

TWO LITTLE BEAVERS

Two little beavers lived in a dam,
One named Sue, the other named
    Sam.
Come to me, Sue; come to me,
    Sam;
Go again, Sue; go again, Sam.

THIS LITTLE PIG WENT TO
MARKET

This little pig went to market;
This little pig stayed at home;
This little pig had roast beef,
This little pig had none;
This little pig cried, "Wee, Wee,
    Wee!" all the way home.

THIS LITTLE PIG WENT TO MARKET

I HAD A LITTLE DOGGIE

I had a little doggie
  That used to sit and beg,
But doggie tumbled downstairs,
  And broke his little leg.
Oh! Doggie, I will nurse you,
  And try to make you well;
And you shall have a collar
  With a pretty bell.

YOU RIDE BEHIND

You ride behind and I'll ride
  before,
And trot, trot away to Baltimore.
You shall take bread and I will
  take honey,
And both of us carry a purse full
  of money.

BLOW, WIND, BLOW!

Blow, wind, blow! and go, mill,
  go!
  That the miller may grind his
    corn;
That the baker may take it,
And into rolls make it,
  And bring us some hot in the
    morn.

SEE-SAW, SACARADOWN

See-saw, sacaradown,
  Which is the way to London
    town?
One foot up, the other foot down,
  Oh, that's the way to London
    town.

22

JACK AND JILL

Jack and Jill went up the hill
To fetch a pail of water;
Jack fell down and broke his crown
And Jill came tumbling after.

CACKLE, CACKLE

Cackle, cackle, Madam Goose!
Have you any feathers loose?
Truly have I, little fellow,
Half enough to fill a pillow;
And here are quills, take one or
    ten,
And make from each popgun or
    pen.

HUSH, BABY, MY DOLL

Hush, baby, my doll, I pray you,
    don't cry,
And I'll give you some bread, and
    some milk by and by;
Or perhaps you like custard, or
    maybe a tart,
Then to either you are welcome,
    with all my heart.

LITTLE TOMMY TITTLE-
MOUSE

Little Tommy Tittlemouse
Lived in a little house.
He caught fishes
In other men's ditches.

I HAD A LITTLE
HOBBY-HORSE

I had a little hobby-horse,
    And it was dapple grey,
Its head was made of pea-straw,
    Its tail was made of hay.

I sold it to an old woman
    For a copper groat;
And I'll not sing my song again
    Without a new coat.

I HAD A LITTLE HOBBY HORSE

HARK, HARK, THE DOGS DO BARK!

Hark, hark, the dogs do bark!
Beggars are coming to town,
Some in rags, some in tags,
And some in velvet gown.

SNEEZE ON MONDAY

Sneeze on Monday, sneeze for
    danger;
Sneeze on Tuesday, kiss a
    stranger;
Sneeze on Wednesday, get a
    letter;
Sneeze on Thursday, something
    better;
Sneeze on Friday, sneeze for
    sorrow;
Sneeze on Saturday, see your
    sweetheart to-morrow.

FOR WANT OF A NAIL

For want of a nail, the shoe was
    lost,
For want of the shoe, the horse
    was lost,
For want of the horse, the rider
    was lost,
For want of the rider, the battle
    was lost,
For want of the battle, the
    kingdom was lost,
And all for the want of a horse-
    shoe nail!

LITTLE DROPS OF WATER

Little drops of water,
    Little grains of sand,
Make the mighty ocean,
    And the pleasant land.

OLD MOTHER GOOSE

Old Mother Goose when
She wanted to wander,

Would ride through the air
On a very fine gander.

COBBLER, COBBLER,
MEND MY SHOE

Cobbler, cobbler, mend my shoe,
And get it done by half-past two:
Stitch it up and stitch it down;
Then I'll give you half a crown.

THANK YOU FOR THE
EARTH SO SWEET

Thank you for the earth so
    sweet,
Thank You for the things we eat,
Thank You for the birds that
    sing,
Thank You, God, for everything.

WHEN LITTLE FRED
WENT TO BED

When little Fred went to bed,
    He always said his prayers;
He kissed mamma, and then
    papa,
    And straightway went up-
      stairs.

A DILLER, A DOLLAR

A diller, a dollar,
A ten o'clock scholar;
What makes you come so soon?
You used to come at ten o'clock,
And now you come at noon.

A DILLER, A DOLLAR, A TEN O'CLOCK SCHOLAR

I'LL SING YOU A SONG

I'll sing you a song,
Though not very long,
   Yet I think it's as pretty as any;
Put your hand in your purse,
You'll never be worse,
   And give the poor singer a
    penny.

A RED SKY IN THE MORNING

A red sky in the morning
Is the shepherd's warning,
A red sky at night
Is the shepherd's delight.

ONE, TWO, THREE, FOUR

One, two, three, four, and five,
I caught a hare alive;
Six, seven, eight, nine, ten,
Then I let him go again.

LADYBIRD, LADYBIRD

Ladybird, ladybird,
Fly away home,
Your house is on fire,
Your children all gone.
All but one, and her name is
   Ann,
And she crept under the
   pudding-pan.

RING-A-RING-A-ROSES

Ring-a-ring-a-roses,
A pocket full of posies;

Hush! Hush! Hush!
We'll all tumble down.

COCK CROWS IN THE MORN

Cock crows in the morn to tell us
  to rise,
And he who lies late will never be
  wise;
For early to bed, and early to rise,
Is the way to be healthy and
  wealthy and wise.

BELL HORSES

Bell horses, bell horses,
  What time o' day,
One o'clock, two o'clock,
  Time to away.

SIMPLE SIMON

Simple Simon met a pieman
  Going to the fair;
Says Simple Simon to the
  pieman,
  "Let me taste your ware."

Says the pieman to Simple
  Simon,
  "Show me first your penny";
Says Simple Simon to the
  pieman,
  "Indeed, I have not any."

SIMPLE SIMON MET A PIEMAN GOING TO THE FAIR

TWINKLE, TWINKLE, LITTLE STAR

Twinkle, twinkle, little star,
How I wonder what you are!
Up above the world so high,
Like a diamond in the sky.

THREE BLIND MICE

Three blind mice, see how they
run!
They all ran after the farmer's
wife,
Who cut off their tails with the
carving-knife,
Did you ever see such a thing in
your life?
As three blind mice.

AS I WAS GOING TO ST. IVES

As I was going to St. Ives,
I met a man with seven wives,
Each wife had seven sacks,
Each sack had seven cats,
Each cat had seven kits,
Kits, cats, sacks, and wives,
How many were there going to
St. Ives?

OUT IN THE WOODS

Out in the woods there is a bird,
Its song the sweetest ever heard;
I saw it in the dogwood dell,
But what it's named I cannot
tell.

PETER, PETER, PUMPKIN-EATER

Peter, Peter, pumpkin-eater,
Had a wife, and couldn't keep her;
He put her in a pumpkin shell,
And there he kept her very well.

THERE WAS A LITTLE GIRL

There was a little girl, and she
    wore a little curl
Right down the middle of her
    forehead;
When she was good, she was
    very, very good,
But when she was bad she was
    horrid.

MARY HAD A PRETTY BIRD

Mary had a pretty bird,
    Feathers bright and yellow,
Slender legs—upon my word,
    He was a pretty fellow.

FOR EVERY EVIL UNDER THE SUN

For every evil under the sun,
There is a remedy, or there is
    none,
If there be one, seek till you find
    it;
If there be none, never mind it.

LITTLE JACK HORNER

Little Jack Horner
    Sat in a corner,
Eating a Christmas pie;
    He put in his thumb,
And pulled out a plum,
    And cried, "What a good boy
    am I!"

LITTLE JACK HORNER SAT IN A CORNER

DEEDLE, DEEDLE, DUMP-LING, MY SON JOHN

Deedle, deedle, dumpling, my son John,
He went to bed with his stockings on,
One shoe off, and one shoe on,
Deedle, deedle, dumpling, my son John.

WHEN JACKY'S A VERY GOOD BOY

When Jacky's a very good boy,
  He shall have cakes and a custard,
But when he does nothing but cry,
  He shall have nothing but mustard.

THIRTY DAYS HATH SEPTEMBER

Thirty days hath September,
April, June, and November;
February has twenty-eight alone,
All the rest have thirty-one;
But Leap Year coming once in four.
February then has one day more.

I HAD A LITTLE HEN

I had a little hen, the prettiest ever seen;
  She washed me the dishes, and kept the house clean;
She went to the mill to fetch me some flour,
  She brought it home in less than an hour.

OLD MOTHER HUBBARD

Old Mother Hubbard,
Went to the cupboard,
  To get her poor dog a bone,

But when she got there,
The cupboard was bare,
  And so the poor dog had none.

LITTLE MAID, PRETTY MAID

Little maid, pretty maid, whither
    goest thou?
"Down in the meadow to milk
    my cow."
Shall I go with thee? "No, not
    now;
When I send for thee, then come
    thou."

JENNY WREN

Jenny Wren last week was wed,
And built her nest in grandpa's
    shed;
Look next week and you shall
    see
Two little eggs, and maybe three.

A LITTLE COCK SPARROW

A little cock sparrow sat on a
    green tree,
    And he chirruped, he chir-
    ruped, so merry was he.

LONDON BRIDGE IS
FALLING DOWN

London Bridge is falling down,
    Falling down, falling down;
London Bridge is falling down,
    My fair lady.

Build it up with wood and clay,
    Wood and clay, wood and clay,
Build it up with wood and clay,
    My fair lady.

LONDON BRIDGE IS FALLING DOWN

TOM, HE WAS A PIPER'S SON

Tom, he was a piper's son,
He learnt to play when he was
young,
But all the tune that he could
play
Was "Over the hills and far
away."
Over the hills, and a great way
off,
And the wind will blow my top-
knot off.

BYE, BABY BUNTING

Bye, baby bunting,
Daddy's gone a-hunting,
To get a little rabbit's skin,
To wrap a baby bunting in.

I'LL TELL YOU A STORY

I'll tell you a story
About Jack of Nory
And now my story's begun,
I'll tell you another
About his brother,
And now my story is done.

LITTLE GIRL, LITTLE GIRL

"Little girl, little girl, where
have you been?"
"Gathering roses to give to the
Queen."

"Little girl, little girl, what
gave she you?"
"She gave me a diamond as big
as my shoe."

LITTLE MISS MUFFET

Little Miss Muffet,
She sat on a tuffet,
Eating of curds and whey;

There came a big spider,
And sat down beside her,
And frightened Miss Muffet away.

WHO'S THAT RINGING AT OUR FRONT DOOR BELL?

Who's that ringing at our front door bell?
I'm a little pussy cat and I'm not very well.

Then put your little nose in a little mutton fat,
And that's the way to cure a little pussy cat.

BIRDS OF A FEATHER

Birds of a feather flock together,
And so will pigs and swine;
Rats and mice will have their choice,
And so will I have mine.

OLD KING COLE

Old King Cole was a merry old soul,
And a merry old soul was he;
He called for his pipe, and he called for his bowl,
And he called for his fiddlers three.

Every fiddler he had a fiddle,
And a very fine fiddle had he;
Twee, tweedle-dee went the fiddlers,
Twee, tweedle-dee, tweedle-dee.
Oh, there's none so rare as can compare
With King Cole and his fiddlers three!

OLD KING COLE WAS A MERRY OLD SOUL

A JOLLY OLD PIG

A jolly old pig once lived in a
  sty,
And three little piggies had she,
And she waddled about saying
  "Grumph! grumph! grumph!"

While the little ones said
  "Wee! wee!"
And she waddled about saying
  "Grumph! grumph! grumph!"
While the little ones said
  "Wee! wee!"

ONE, TWO, THREE, FOUR, FIVE

One, two, three, four, five,
I caught a fish alive.
Why did you let it go?
Because it bit my finger so.

LITTLE STAR THAT SHINES SO BRIGHT

Little star that shines so bright,
Come and peep at me tonight,
For I often watch for you
In the pretty sky so blue.

Little star! O tell me, pray,
Where you hide yourself all day?
Have you got a home like me,
And a father kind to see?

MULTIPLICATION IS VEXATION

Multiplication is vexation,
  Division is as bad;
The Rule of Three doth puzzle
  me,
  And Practice drives me mad.

Little Child, at you I peep
While you lie so fast asleep;
But when morn begins to break,
I my homeward journey take.

LEG OVER LEG

Leg over leg,
As the dog went to Dover;
  When he came to a stile,
Jump he went over.

For I've many friends on high,
Living with me in the sky;
And a loving Father, too,
Who commands what I'm to do.

BARBER, BARBER, SHAVE A PIG

Barber, barber, shave a pig,
How many hairs will make a wig?
"Four and twenty, that's enough."
Give the poor barber a pinch of snuff.

RAIN, RAIN, GO AWAY

Rain, rain, go away,
Come again another day;
Little Johnny wants to play.

AH! HEAR THE WIND BLOW!

Ah! hear the wind blow!
And see the deep snow!
Where now are the birds we love
   to hear sing?

They are where it's warm,
They are free of all harm.
They will come back again in
   the spring, in the spring.

RIDDLE-ME, RIDDLE-ME, REE

Riddle-me, riddle-me, ree,
   A hawk sat up on a tree;
And he says to himself, says he,
Oh dear what a fine bird I be!

WEE WILLIE WINKIE

Wee Willie Winkie runs through
   the town,
Upstairs and downstairs in his
   night-gown,
Rapping at the window, crying
   through the lock
"Are the children all in bed for
   it's now eight o'clock?"

WEE WILLIE WINKIE RUNS THROUGH THE TOWN

SMILING GIRLS, ROSY BOYS

Smiling girls, rosy boys,
    Come and buy my little toys;
Monkeys made of ginger bread,
    And sugar horses painted red.

THE NORTH WIND
DOTH BLOW

The north wind doth blow,
And we shall have snow,
And what will poor Robin do
    then?
    Poor thing!

He'll sit in the barn,
And keep himself warm,
And hide his head under his
    wing.
    Poor thing!

BOW-WOW, SAYS THE
DOG

Bow-wow, says the dog;
    Mew, mew, says the cat;
Grunt, grunt, goes the hog;
    And squeak, says the rat.

Tu-whu, says the owl;
    Caw, caw, says the crow;
Quack, quack, goes the duck;
    And moo, says the cow.

SWAN, SWIM, OVER
THE SEA

Swan, swim, over the sea
    Swim, swan, swim!
Swan, swim back again;
    Well swam swan!

BOW, WOW, WOW

Bow, wow, wow,
Whose dog are thou?

Little Tommy Tinker's dog,
Bow, wow, wow.

RIDE AWAY, RIDE AWAY

Ride away, ride away, Donald
    shall ride,
Ride to the city to get him a bride;

She shall be gentle, she shall be
    fair,
With gems on her fingers, and
    plumes in her hair.

THE MAN IN THE MOON LOOKED OUT OF THE MOON

The Man in the Moon looked out
    of the moon,
And this is what he said:
"It's time that, now I am getting
    up,
All children are in bed."

HERE'S SULKY SUE

Here's Sulky Sue,
What shall we do?
Turn her face to the wall
Till she comes to.

THREE LITTLE KITTENS

Three little kittens, they lost
    their mittens,
    And they began to cry,
"Oh, mother, dear, we greatly
    fear,
That we have lost our mittens."

"What! lost your mittens, you
    naughty kittens!
Then you shall have no pie."
Mee-ow, mee-ow, mee-ow,
    mee-ow,
    Then you shall have no pie.

THREE LITTLE KITTENS, THEY LOST THEIR MITTENS

AN APPLE PIE

An apple pie, when it looks nice,
Would make one long to have a
    slice;
And if the taste should prove so,
    too,
I fear one slice would hardly do.
So to prevent my asking twice,
Pray, mamma, cut a good big
    slice.

WHEN I WAS A LITTLE
GIRL

When I was a little girl, I washed
    my mammy's dishes:
Now I am a big girl, I roll in
    golden riches.

OLD DR. FOSTER

Old Dr. Foster
Went to Glo'ster
In a shower of rain;
He stepped in a puddle,
Up to the middle,
And never went there again.

PETER PIPER

Peter Piper picked a peck of
    pickled pepper;
A peck of pickled pepper
Peter Piper picked;
If Peter Piper picked a peck of
    pickled pepper,
Where's the peck of pickled
    pepper Peter Piper picked?

LITTLE TOM TUCKER

Little Tom Tucker,
Sings for his supper;
What shall he eat?
White bread and butter;

How will he cut it without a knife?
How will he be married without a wife?

SEE-SAW, MARGERY DAW

See-saw, Margery Daw,
Jacky shall have a new master;
Jacky must have but a penny a
   day,
Because he can work no faster.

LITTLE FOLKS

Little folks, little folks,
Now then for bed!
A pillow is waiting
For each little head.

Sleep all the night,
And wake in the morn;
Robert shall sound
The call on his horn.

ONE, TWO, BUCKLE MY SHOE

One, two, buckle my shoe;
Three, four, shut the door;
Five, six, pick up sticks;
Seven, eight, lay them straight;
Nine, ten, a good fat hen.

PAT A CAKE

"Pat a cake, pat a cake,
   Baker's man."
"Bake me a cake,
   As fast as you can."
"Pat it and prick it,
   And mark it with a T,
And put in the oven
   For Tommy and me."

PAT A CAKE, PAT A CAKE, BAKER'S MAN

DIDDLEDY, DIDDLEDY, DUMPTY

Diddledy, diddledy, dumpty:
The cat ran up the plum-tree.
    I'll lay you a crown
    I'll fetch you down;
So diddledy, diddledy, dumpty.

BRING THE HOOP

Bring the hoop, and bring the
   ball,
Come with happy faces all;
Let us make a merry ring,
Talk and laugh, and dance and
   sing;
Quickly, quickly, come away,
For it is a pleasant day.

CHRISTMAS COMES BUT ONCE A YEAR

Christmas comes but once a year,
And when it comes it brings good
   cheer.

I HAD A LITTLE PONY

I had a little pony,
   They called him Dapple-gray;
I lent him to a lady,
   To ride a mile away.

She whipped him, she slashed
   him,
   She rode him through the mire;
I would not lend my pony now,
   For all the lady's hire.

THERE WAS AN OLD WOMAN

There was an old woman who
    lived in a shoe,
She had so many children she
    didn't know what to do;

She gave them some broth with-
    out any bread,
And whipped them all well, and
    put them to bed.

THREE WISE MEN OF GOTHAM

Three wise men of Gotham,
They went to sea in a bowl,
And if the bowl had been stronger
My song had been longer.

WASN'T IT FUNNY?

Wasn't it funny? hear it, all
  people!
Little Tom Thumb has swal-
  lowed a steeple!

How did he do it?
I'll tell you, my son!
'Twas made of white sugar—and
  easily done!

CHRISTMAS IS COMING

Christmas is coming, the geese
  are getting fat;
Please put a penny in the old
  man's hat.

BOBBY SHAFTOE'S GONE TO SEA

Bobby Shaftoe's gone to sea,
Silver buckles on his knee;
He'll come back and marry me,
  Pretty Bobby Shaftoe.

Bobby Shaftoe's fat and fair,
Combing down his auburn hair;
He's my love for evermore;
  Pretty Bobby Shaftoe.

BOBBY SHAFTOE'S GONE TO SEA

I LOVE YOU WELL

I love you well, my little brother,
   And you are fond of me;
Let us be kind to one another,
   As brothers ought to be.
You shall learn to play with me,
   And learn to use my toys;
And then I think that we shall be
   Two happy little boys.

HOW MANY DAYS HAS MY BABY TO PLAY?

How many days has my baby to
   play?
   Saturday, Sunday, Monday,
Tuesday, Wednesday, Thursday,
   Friday,
   Saturday, Sunday, Monday.

HANDY-SPANDY

Handy-Spandy, Jack-a-dandy,
Loved plum-cake and sugar-
   candy.
He bought some at a grocer's
   shop,
And out he came, hop, hop, hop.

ONCE I SAW A LITTLE BIRD

Once I saw a little bird
   Come hop, hop, hop;
So I cried, "Little bird,
   Will you stop, stop, stop?"
And was going to the window
   To say, "How do you do?"
But he shook his little tail,
   And far away he flew.

HEY! DIDDLE, DIDDLE!

Hey! diddle, diddle! The cat and the fiddle,
The cow jumped over the moon;
The little dog laughed to see such sport,
And the dish ran away with the spoon.

LITTLE MAIDEN

Little maiden,
Better tarry;
Time enough next year to marry.
Hearts may change,
And so may fancy;
Wait a little longer, Nancy.

POLLY-GALLENA

Polly-gallena, my fat hen,
Laid ivory eggs a score and ten;
Many good people call every day,
To look at the eggs my hen doth
  lay.

THE KING OF IAN

The King of Ian was very fat,
Had a crown, but not a hat;
Oh, what a king was that, was
  that!
Oh rat, tat, tat; oh rat, tat, tat.

HERE WE GO

Here we go up, up, up,
Here we go down, down, down,
Here we go backward and
  forward,
And here we **go round, round,**
  round.

RIDE A COCK-HORSE

Ride a cock-horse
To Banbury Cross,
To see a fair lady ride on a white
  horse;
Rings on her fingers and bells on
  her toes,
She shall have music wherever
  she goes.

JACK SPRAT

Jack Sprat could eat no fat,
  His wife could eat no lean;
And so betwixt them both, you
  see,
  They licked the platter clean.

PUSSY-CAT, PUSSY-CAT

Pussy-cat, pussy-cat, where have
  you been?
I've been to London to look at
  the Queen.
Pussy-cat, pussy-cat, what did
  you there?
I frightened a little mouse under
  the chair.

PUSSY CAT, PUSSY CAT, WHERE HAVE YOU BEEN?

BILLY, BILLY, COME AND PLAY

"Billy, Billy, come and play,
While the sun shines bright as
  day."
"Yes, my Polly, so I will,
For I love to please you still."

THERE WAS A CROOKED MAN

There was a crooked man, and
  he went a crooked mile,
And he found a crooked sixpence
  against a crooked stile;
He bought a crooked cat, which
  caught a crooked mouse,
And they all lived together in a
  little crooked house.

THEY THAT WASH ON MONDAY

They that wash on Monday
Have all the week to dry;
They that wash on Tuesday
  Are not so much awry;
They that wash on Wednesday
  Are not so much to blame;
They that wash on Thursday,
  Wash for shame;
They that wash on Friday,
  Wash in need;
And they that wash on Saturday
  Are lazy folks indeed.

MARCH WINDS

March winds and April
  showers
Bring forth May flowers.

HIPPETY HOP TO THE
BARBER SHOP

Hippety hop to the barber shop,
To get a stick of candy,
One for you and one for me,
And one for Sister Mandy.

A CAT CAME FIDDLING

A cat came fiddling out of a barn,
With a pair of bag-pipes under
　her arm:
She could sing nothing but fiddle
　cum fee,
The mouse has married the
　bumble-bee;
Pipe, cat,—dance, mouse,
We'll have a wedding at our fine
　house.

TOMMY TROT

Tommy Trot, a man of law,
Sold his bed and lay upon straw;
Sold the straw, and slept on
　grass,
To buy his wife a looking-glass.

GREAT "A", LITTLE "A"

Great "A", Little "A",
　Bouncing "B".
The cat's in the cupboard,
　And can't see me.

CROSS PATCH

Cross patch
　Draw the latch,
Sit by the fire and spin;
　Take a cup
　And drink it up,
Then call your neighbors in.

PIT, PAT, WELL-A-DAY

Pit, pat, well-a-day,
Little Robin flew away.
Where can little Robin be?
Gone into the cherry tree.

I LIKE LITTLE PUSSY

I like little pussy, her coat is so
　warm,
And if I don't hurt her she'll do
　me no harm;
So I'll not pull her tail, nor drive
　her away,
But pussy and I very gently will
　play.

I LIKE LITTLE PUSSY, HER COAT IS SO WARM

ROBERT BARNES, FELLOW FINE

"Robert Barnes, fellow fine,
Can you shoe this horse of
    mine?"
"Yes, good Sir, that I can,
As well as any other man;
There's a nail, and there's a prod,
And now, good Sir, your horse is
    shod."

ONE TO MAKE READY

One to make ready,
    And two to prepare;
Good luck to the rider,
    And away goes the mare.

EARLY TO BED

Early to bed, early to rise,
Makes a man healthy,
    wealthy and wise.

HOT-CROSS BUNS!

Hot-cross buns! Hot-cross buns!
One a penny, two a penny,
    Hot-cross buns!
If you have no daughters,
Give them to your sons,
One a penny, two a penny,
    Hot-cross buns!
But if you have none of these
    little elves,
Then you may eat them all your-
    selves.

HUMPTY-DUMPTY

Humpty-Dumpty sat on a wall,
Humpty-Dumpty had a great fall;
All the King's horses, and all the King's men,
Could not put Humpty-Dumpty together again.

HICKETY PICKETY, MY BLACK HEN

Hickety Pickety, my black hen,
She lays eggs for gentlemen;
Gentlemen come every day
To see what my black hen
  doth lay.
Sometimes nine, and sometimes
  ten,
Hickety Pickety, my fat hen.

JEREMIAH, BLOW THE FIRE

Jeremiah, blow the fire,
Puff, puff, puff!
First you blow it gently,
Then you blow it rough.

I HAD TWO PIGEONS

I had two pigeons bright and
  gay;
They flew from me the other day;
What was the reason they did
  go?
I cannot tell, for I do not know.

BAA, BAA, BLACK SHEEP

Baa, baa, black sheep,
  Have you any wool?
Yes, sir, yes, sir, three bags full:
One for my master,
  One for my dame,
And one for the little boy
  Who lives down the lane.

BAA, BAA, BLACK SHEEP, HAVE YOU ANY WOOL?

CURLY LOCKS! CURLY LOCKS!

Curly locks! Curly locks! wilt
  thou be mine?
Thou shalt not wash dishes, nor
  yet feed the swine;
But sit on a cushion and sew a
  fine seam,
And feed upon strawberries,
  sugar, and cream.

MIND YOUR COMMAS

Every lady in this land
Has twenty nails, upon each
  hand
Five, and twenty on hands and
  feet,
All this is true, without deceit.

PEASE-PORRIDGE HOT

Pease-porridge hot,
Pease-porridge cold,
Pease-porridge in the pot, nine
  days old.

Spell me that without a p
And a clever scholar you will be.

I HAD A LITTLE DOG

I had a little dog, and his name
  was Blue Bell,
I gave him some work, and he did
  it very well;
I sent him upstairs to pick up a
  pin,
He stepped in the coal-scuttle up
  to his chin.

TOM, TOM, THE PIPER'S SON

Tom, Tom, the piper's son,
Stole a pig and away did run!
The pig was eat, and Tom was beat,
Till he ran crying down the street.

COME, LET'S TO BED

Come, let's to bed,
Says Sleepy-head;
Tarry awhile, says Slow;
Put on the pan,
Says Greedy Nan,
Let's sup before we go.

SPEAK KINDLY

Speak kindly to your dog, my
    boy!
All things that live know pain
    and joy.
Speak harshly to your dog and
    see
How sad and shamed he seems
    to be;
His **head, and ears,** and tail all
    say,
Oh! let me go far, far away!

IS JOHN SMITH WITHIN?

"Is John Smith within?"
    "Yes, that he is,"
"Can he set a shoe?"
    "Aye, marry, two.
Here a nail, there a nail,
    Tick, tack, too."

DING, DONG BELL

Ding, dong bell,
The cat's in the well!
Who put her in?
Little Johnny Green.
Who pulled her out?
Little Tommy Stout.
What a naughty boy was that,
To drown poor pussy cat,
Who never did any harm,
And killed the mice in his
    father's barn.

DING, DONG BELL, THE CAT'S IN THE WELL!

COME HITHER, SWEET ROBIN

Come hither, sweet robin,
And be not afraid,
I would not hurt even a
    feather;
Come hither, sweet robin,
And pick up some bread,
To feed you this very cold
    weather.

SEE A PIN AND PICK IT UP

See a pin and pick it up,
All the day you'll have good luck.
See a pin and let it lay,
Bad luck you'll have all the day.

POOR OLD ROBINSON CRUSOE!

Poor old Robinson Crusoe!
    Poor old Robinson Crusoe!
They made him a coat of an old
    Nanny goat,
    I wonder how they could do so!
With a ring-a-ting-tang, and a
    ring-a-ting-tang,
    Poor old Robinson Crusoe!

YANKEE DOODLE

Yankee Doodle went to town,
Riding on a pony,
Stuck a feather in his hat,
And called him Macaroni.

THE MULBERRY BUSH

Here we go round the mulberry bush,
The mulberry bush, the mulberry bush,
Here we go round the mulberry bush,
On a cold and frosty morning.

THE BUNCH OF BLUE RIBBONS

Oh, dear, what can the matter
    be?
Oh, dear, what can the matter
    be?
Oh, dear, what can the matter
    be?
    Johnny's so long at the fair.
He promised he'd buy me a bunch
    of blue ribbons,
He promised he'd buy me a bunch
    of blue ribbons,
He promised he'd buy me a bunch
    of blue ribbons,
    To tie up my bonny brown hair.

BLACK WITHIN

Black within, and red without:
Four corners round about.
          (A chimney)

SING A SONG OF SIXPENCE

Sing a song of sixpence,
  A pocket full of rye;
Four and twenty blackbirds
  Baked in a pie.

When the pie was opened,
  The birds began to sing;
Was not that a dainty dish
  To set before the king?

The king was in his counting-
    house
  Counting out his money;
The queen was in the parlor
  Eating bread and honey;

The maid was in the garden
  Hanging out the clothes,
There came a little blackbird,
  And snapped off her nose.

SING A SONG OF SIXPENCE, A POCKET FULL OF RYE

DICKERY, DICKERY, DARE

Dickery, dickery, dare,
  The pig flew up in the air;
The man in brown soon brought
  him down,
Dickery, dickery, dare.

UP THE LADDER

Up the ladder and down the wall,
A halfpenny roll will serve us
  all.
You find milk, and I'll find flour,
And we'll have a pudding in half
  an hour.

TO MARKET, TO MARKET

To market, to market,
To buy a penny bun,
Home again, home again,
Market is done.

EENA, MEENA, MINAH, MO

Eena, meena, minah, mo,
Catch an Indian by his toe,
If he halloos, let him go,
Eena, meena, minah, mo,
O—U—T spells out!

MISTRESS MARY, QUITE CONTRARY

Mistress Mary,
Quite contrary,
How does your garden grow?
With silver bells,
And cockleshells,
And pretty maids all in a row.

OH, WHERE, OH, WHERE IS MY LITTLE DOG GONE?

Oh, where, oh, where is my
  little dog gone?
  Oh, where, oh, where can
  he be?
With his ears cut short and his
  tail cut long,
  Oh, where, oh, where is he?

LITTLE TEE WEE

Little Tee Wee,
He went to sea
In an open boat;
And while afloat
The little boat bended,
And my story's ended.

SUMMER BREEZE

Summer breeze, so softly blow-
  ing,
In my garden pinks are growing;
If you go and send the showers,
You may come and smell my
  flowers.

AS I WAS GOING ALONG

As I was going along, long, long,
  long,
A-singing a comical song, song,
  song,
The lane that I went was so long,
  long, long,
And the song that I sung was so
  long, long, long,
And so I went singing along.

HICKORY, DICKORY, DOCK

Hickory, dickory, dock!
The mouse ran up the clock;

The clock struck one, and down
he ran, Hickory, dickory, dock!

MOLLY, MY SISTER, AND I FELL OUT

Molly, my sister, and I fell out,
And what do you think it was all
    about?
She loved coffee and I loved tea,
And that was the reason we
    couldn't agree.

JACK, BE NIMBLE

Jack, be nimble,
Jack, be quick,
And Jack, jump over the
    candle-stick.

LITTLE WIND

Little wind, blow on the hill top;
Little wind, blow down the plain;
Little wind, blow up the sun-
    shine;
Little wind, blow off the rain.

I'M GLAD THE SKY IS PAINTED BLUE

I'm glad the sky is painted blue,
And earth is painted green,
With such a lot of nice fresh air
All sandwiched in between.

COCK-A-DOODLE-DOO

Cock-a-doodle-doo!
My dame has lost her shoe,
And master's lost his fiddling
    stick,
And doesn't know what to do.

SING, SING

Sing, sing, what shall I sing?
Baby has gotten a new gold ring;
Yellow and brilliant, brilliant
    and yellow,
Baby, our darling, is a dear little
    fellow.

GEORGIE PORGIE

Georgie Porgie, pudding and pie,
Kissed the girls and made them cry;
When the boys came out to play,
Georgie Porgie ran away.

A DOG AND A CAT

A dog and a cat went out together,
    To see some friends just out of
    the town;
Said the cat to the dog, "What
    d'ye think of the weather?"

"I think, ma'am, the rain will
    come down—
But don't be alarmed, for I've an
    umbrella
That will shelter us both," said
    this amiable fellow.

HUSH-A-BY, BABY

Hush-a-by, baby, on the tree top,
When the wind blows, the cradle
    will rock,
When the bough bends, the
    cradle will fall,
Down will come baby, bough,
    cradle, and all.

ONE, TWO, THREE

One, two, three,
    I love coffee,
        And Billy loves tea.
How good you be,
    One, two, three;
        I love coffee,
            And Billy loves tea.

LUCY LOCKET

Lucy Locket
Lost her pocket,
Kitty Fisher found it;

Nothing in it,
Nothing in it,
But the binding round it.

LOOK AT MY DOG

Look at my dog. I call him Pink.
Now sit up, Pink, and do not
wink,
Look in my eyes! Steady, steady!
Hear the command! Are you
ready?
Now, sir, attend! When I say
four,
You'll walk three steps, and shut
the door!

LITTLE BETTY BLUE

Little Betty Blue
Lost her holiday shoe,
What can little Betty do?
Give her another,
To match the other,
And then she may walk in two.

UP THE HILL

Up the hill take care of me;
Down the hill take care of thee;
Give me no water when I am
hot;
In the stable forget me not.

(a horse)

POLLY, PUT THE KETTLE ON

Polly, put the kettle on,
Polly, put the kettle on,
Polly, put the kettle on,
And let's drink tea.

Sukey, take it off again,
Sukey, take it off again,
Sukey, take it off again,
They're all gone away.

TO MARKET, TO MARKET

To market, to market, to buy a
  fat pig,
Home again, home again, jiggety
  jig;

To market, to market, to buy a
  fat hog,
Home again, home again, jiggety
  jog.

About the Artist

THE ILLUSTRATIONS of this book, bright and gay and presenting so admirably the nursery world of Mother Goose, are the work of Margot Austin. As a girl Mrs. Austin attended St. Mary's Academy in Portland, Oregon, the city of her birth. Later her interest in art took her to New York, where she studied at the National Academy of Design and the Grand Central School of Art. Her books and illustrations for children quickly won her a secure place in children's literature, and a number of her books have become widely-acclaimed favorites.

Nowhere is the versatility of Margot Austin's talent better displayed than in her illustrations for Mother Goose rhymes. She has portrayed these timeless characters in many styles, varying from dainty tapestry-like figures to plump robust characters, in settings full of amusing detail. But of them all, perhaps, the charming toylike figures of this deluxe volume most successfully recreate the favorite Mother Goose characters of the child's world.

That Margot Austin prefers the simplicity of her 200-year-old Connecticut farm to any other place in the world, that her favorite interests, in addition to her artist-husband and her son, are other people's dogs and cats, and that she has no elaborate system of work, all may help to explain the directness and simplicity that are characteristic of her art.

Whatever has brought it about, there is no doubt that Margot Austin has captured the very spirit of the nursery with the figures that adorn *The Very Young Mother Goose*.